New Forewoı

FOR more than 150 years the Vulcan Works in Newton-le-Willows, Lancashire, England, became synonymous with the railway industry, and Lancashire's reputation throughout the British Empire as being the workshop of the world was never more true than in this tiny corner of the county.

Between 1853 and 1953 a total of 2,750 locomotives left the works for India, or an average of one every two weeks, which was an astonishing feat! But, as this book shows, steam trains were also sent to Africa, Argentina, Burma, Iran, Iraq and numerous other nations throughout the world, each of the trains being manufactured to the specifications demanded by the individual countries according to terrain and preference. The fact is, that whatever countries or colonies wanted, Vulcan willingly supplied, and even today some of those trains are still in existence, indeed running, which is a tribute to the skilled workforce that produced them.

A railway line had been built alongside the Vulcan Works, allowing easy access to the main railway network, and as early as 1835 engines were being sent as far afield as the United States, Russia and Austria, and the reputation of the company was assured.

By 1914 Vulcan was fully established as a manufacturing base, and in the year the First World War broke out the works produced its 3,000th locomotive, with its 4,000th steam train leaving the premises only 11 years later. During the war the company had diverted resources to manufacturing weapons and ammunition.

The Vulcan Works produced its last locomotive in 1970 for Ghana Railways before moving to the production of diesel engines for traction, marine and industrial purposes. But the heady days of steam established the company, and this book is a reminder of those days. The steam era is no more, and neither, alas, is Vulcan Works, for it closed down completely in 2001. It is a sad loss to Lancashire, but a greater loss still to those who worked there and this book, (which first appeared in 1955 merely as a portion of an internal brochure for potential clients and employees) is a tribute to them all. It is also our intention in the near future to produce a similar work outlining the diesel and electric locomotives manufactured in Vulcan Works, thus completing our tribute.

Peter Riley

Acknowledgements

The publishers would like to thank the following for their help during
the preparation of this book

Jo Unsworth, Senior Librarian, Warrington Library
Louise Jameson, archivist of Marconi Plc
without whom this book would not have been possible

Vulcan Steam Locomotives

A collection of steam trains produced at the famous
Vulcan locomotive works in Lancashire, England

P & D Riley

First published in 1955 by The Vulcan Foundry Limited as part of
Vulcan Locomotives, a promotional publication not available for public sale.

This edition first published 2003 by

P & D Riley
12 Bridgeway East
Cheshire
WA7 6LD
England.

By permission of Marconi plc

This edition © Marconi plc & P & D Riley

ISBN:1 874712 65 4

British Library Cataloguing in Publication Data
A catalogue record for this book is available from the British Library

Printed in England.

ORIGINAL FOREWORD

Early in 1955, The Vulcan Foundry Limited and its Associate Company, Robert Stephenson & Hawthorns Limited, were invited to become Members of The English Electric Group of Companies, and Vulcan is proud to announce that on March 17th 1955, this membership became an accomplished fact.

For a number of years since the second World War, Vulcan and Stephensons have collaborated harmoniously with The English Electric Company in the manufacture of mechanical parts for electric and diesel electric locomotives. Now, with the increasing trend towards motive power of these types, Vulcan will be concentrating still further on this aspect of its production and the collaboration will be amplified and become even closer.

The English Electric Group, known throughout the world for the manufacture by its members of a wide variety of industrial products, ranging from aircraft, locomotives, and electric generating equipment, to everyday domestic appliances, is unique among British Locomotive Manufacturers in being able to build power units, locomotives and trains all in its own Works. This ensures for the customer, maximum co-ordination in the design of mechanical parts, diesel engines, and electrical equipment. Complete railway electrification schemes are also undertaken and have been carried out all over the world.

In joining The English Electric Group, Vulcan and Stephensons, with a wealth of tradition behind them, will by no means be losing their individuality. The union is an important step in the development of a vital branch of modern British Industry, and it will react to the benefit of all.

This brochure illustrates something of what has been done at Vulcan in the past and indicates also its potentialities for the future.

HOW TO REACH THE WORKS

BY RAIL : We are always pleased to send a car to one of the nearby stations to meet our visitors. Travellers from London (Euston) should come to Warrington (Bank Quay) Station, which is about four miles from the Works. There is a good service from both Liverpool (Lime Street) and Manchester (Exchange) to either Newton-le-Willows or Earlestown Stations, which are equally convenient for the Works, while Warrington (Central) is the best arrival point from certain directions, such as Sheffield.

BY ROAD : From the SOUTH, take the main Wigan road from Warrington (A.49) and after three miles fork left at the Swan Hotel (on right) and immediately turn **left.** Follow this road until it leads up to a bridge over the railway, and turn **right** just before reaching the bridge, on to a side-road which leads to the Works. Bear left through Vulcan Village, and the Offices are immediately opposite the Railway Halt.

From *the* NORTH, approaching from Wigan on A.49, cross the East Lancashire Road (A.580) and take first turn **right** (after one mile) at the Oak Tree Inn, Newton-le-Willows. After half a mile, turn **left** into Victoria Road, then straight through to the Works.

From MANCHESTER, leave by A.6 to Irlam O'th'Heights, fork left on to the East Lancashire Road (A.580) for 11 miles, then turn **left** (signposted to Warrington) on to A.572. After two miles turn **right** at the Legh Arms on to the main Wigan road (A.49), take first **left,** and first **left** again, into Park Road. Straight along (passing under railway bridge) for three-quarters of a mile, and turn **left** at "T" junction, reaching the Works a few hundred yards along this road.

From LIVERPOOL, reach the East Lancashire Road (A.580), and after 17 miles turn **right** on to A.49 at Haydock Roundabout, and continue as shown from the North.

The above routes are shown on the map reproduced on the opposite page.

BY AIR : The most convenient airport is Ringway (Manchester), a road journey of roughly one hour from the Works.

Visitors coming from London are invited to get into touch with our London Office Manager at 82 Victoria Street, S.W.I (telephone Victoria 8778) who will be only too pleased to do anything he can to help in regard to travelling or hotel arrangements.

LOCATION OF VULCAN WORKS

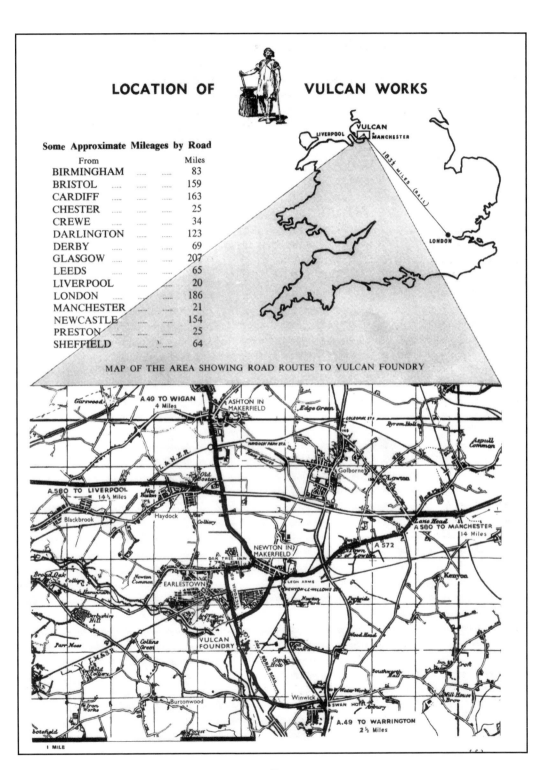

Some Approximate Mileages by Road

From			Miles
BIRMINGHAM	......	......	83
BRISTOL			159
CARDIFF	......	......	163
CHESTER	......		25
CREWE	......		34
DARLINGTON			123
DERBY	......		69
GLASGOW	......		207
LEEDS	......	......	65
LIVERPOOL	......	......	20
LONDON	......	......	186
MANCHESTER			21
NEWCASTLE	......	......	154
PRESTON	......		25
SHEFFIELD	......	......	64

MAP OF THE AREA SHOWING ROAD ROUTES TO VULCAN FOUNDRY

HISTORICAL NOTE

The Vulcan Foundry was founded in 1830 by Robert Stephenson in collaboration with Charles Tayleur, a Liverpool engineer. Robert Stephenson was already managing a Locomotive Works in Newcastle-on-Tyne, but finding it

The "Tayleur"

virtually impossible to transport locomotives from his Newcastle factory to Lancashire for use on the newly constructed Liverpool and Manchester Railway, he decided to go into partnership with Tayleur with a view to building engines on the spot, and a site was chosen half way between the two cities, at Newton-le-Willows.

The first locomotive to be built at Vulcan Foundry was produced for the North Union Railway and was named " Tayleur," and this was followed shortly afterwards by three more for the Warrington and Newton Railway opened in 1831.

Vulcan were soon b u i l d i n g locomotives for many of the new railways which were springing up all over Great Britain and they were also very early in the export market.

By 1840 engines had been sent to no fewer than five Continental countries and even to the U.S.A.— early dollar earners indeed.

In 1847, a subsidiary firm, the Bank Quay Foundry, was taken over. This foundry had been operating in Warrington since 1834 and it was here that the materials for such enterprises as the Conway Bridge and the Britannia Bridge over the Menai Straits were prepared. The first iron seagoing vessel, " Tayleur," a tea clipper, was also built at Bank Quay Foundry.

Locomotive building proceeded apace and many famous locomotive engineers were connected with The Vulcan Foundry, including William Kirtley, H. Dubs, and Sir Daniel Gooch.

Building the Conway Bridge

The first Iron Sea-going Vessel 'Tayleur'

In 1852 the Firm's longstanding connection with India commenced with the export of eight 2-4-0 passenger locomotives to the Great Indian Peninsula Railway. These engines opened the first public railway in India, from Bombay to Thana in 1853, an event which was suitably commemorated by the Indian Railways Centenary Exhibition at New Delhi during March and April 1953. Between 1852 and 1952 Vulcan supplied nearly 2,750 locomotives for service in India, an average of more than one a fortnight for 100 years.

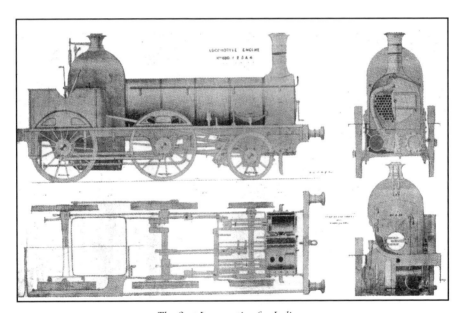

The first Locomotive for India

In 1871 Vulcan built the first locomotive to run in Japan, and since those early days Vulcan locomotives have become so well known owing to the excellence of the materials with which they are constructed and the accuracy and precision of their workmanship, that there is hardly a country in the world where they are not to be found.

Outstanding among the productions of the inter-war years were the Standard locomotives for India. After building many of the earlier B.E.S.A. semi-standard engines, Vulcan played a large part in assisting the Government of India with their great standardisation drive in the 1920's, and subsequently large numbers of both the broad and metre gauge types evolved, were turned out at Newton-le-Willows.

The first Locomotive in Japan

During the 1914-1918 War a great deal of armament work was undertaken and for some years prior to World War II and up to 1943, the Works were engaged on the production of tanks and other munitions for the War Department, together with torpedoes and gun mechanisms, etc., for the Admiralty.

A large amount of the design work for the Matilda tank was entrusted to the Firm and subsequently nearly 3,000 were either built at Newton or manufactured by other Companies to Vulcan jigs and gauges and under their guidance.

Pre-Standard 4-6-0 Express Locomotive "Hero" G.I.P. Ry

In 1943, however, production reverted to locomotives and 390 of the Austerity 2-8-0 type were constructed to the orders of the Ministry of Supply for the use of the War Department. With the end of hostilities, locomotive manufacture for the export drive was soon in full swing once more, and since then a steady stream of locomotives has crossed the seas from Newton-le-Willows, carrying the fame of Lancashire craftsmanship to five continents.

The foregoing remarks have dwelt principally on steam locomotives, but this is perhaps inevitable since Vulcan's earlier history is bound up almost exclusively with this form of motive power.

The Works

View of the Vulcan Foundry

The Works are situated about four miles north of Warrington, Lancashire, and about one mile from both Earlestown and Newton-le-Willows, both of which are on the London Midland Region main line railway between Liverpool and Manchester.

As already stated, Vulcan have built locomotives since 1830, and during this long period many and varied types, steam, diesel, and electric, have been constructed for all gauges, countries, and climatic conditions, and with weights ranging from a few tons up to 200 tons.

The design work is in the hands of qualified experts who appreciate its supreme importance and devote to it the greatest care, ensuring that the latest known practices are incorporated to provide the best possible performance and the greatest facility of maintenance.

During the building of the locomotives in the Shops, all parts are manufactured under strict supervision and are machined accurately to specified limits and fits. They are subsequently checked by a competent inspection staff to ensure interchangeability so that when assembled, reliable and satisfactory service is assured.

The Works themselves occupy an area of 87 acres, 15 of them covered by buildings, and up to 3,500 workmen are employed. They are spacious, airy, and well lighted, and special attention is paid to all aspects of the welfare of the employees.

A few details of the shop layout will be of interest as an illustration of the very up to date facilities available.

The Pattern and Joiners Shop covers 18,530 sq. ft. and in addition to patterns and wooden locomotive fittings, all packing cases are made on the premises.

In the entirely new Non-ferrous Foundry, 8 to 10 tons of general castings are produced weekly from modern Morgan Crucible type furnaces.

INDIAN RAILWAYS

5ft 6in Gauge   **1928-35**   **4-6-2 (XA)**

Cylinders	(2) 18 in. Diam. X 26 in. Stroke	Maximum Axleload	13-1 tons
Diameter Coupled Wheels	5 ft. 1½ in.	Weight :	
Working Pressure	180 lb.	Engine in Working Order	67-15 „
Tractive Effort at 85% Pressure	20,960 lb.	Tender "	42-1 „
		Total "	109-25 „

In the 1920's, many of the major Indian Railways began to come under the control of the Indian Government. It was then decided to carry out a large measure of locomotive standardisation, and a special committee was appointed to lay down the general designs of the various types required. Details of these engines were worked out by the Locomotive Industry in conjunction with the consulting engineers, The Vulcan Foundry playing a leading part, and in 1926 tenders were called for from the leading manufacturers.

The locomotive illustrated above is one of the XA Class of 4-6-2 Pacifies specially designed for branch line passenger work where the maximum axleload is limited to 13 tons.

Between 1928 and 1935, 113 of this type were constructed at The Vulcan Foundry for the major Indian railways under government control, especially the then G.I.P. Railway and the North Western Railway, the latter now part of the Pakistan system.

In order to cope with the low grade Indian coal, the new Standard passenger and goods locomotives were all provided with a hind truck in order to accommodate a wide firebox with large grate area. The general design, which retained the use of plate frames, was straightforward and robust and all accessories were made as simple as possible.

NORTH WESTERN RAILWAY, PAKISTAN

| 5ft 6in Gauge | 1930 | 4-6-2 (XS1 & XS2) |

Cylinders	**(4) 16 in. Diam. X 26 in. Stroke**	Maximum Axleload	**21·5 tons**	
Diameter Coupled Wheels	**6 ft. 2 in.**	Weight :		
Working Pressure	**225 lb.**	Engine in working order	**108**	"
		Tender " "	**64-15**	"
Tractive Effort at 85% Pressure	**34,400 lb.**	Total " "	**172-15**	"

In 1928 four experimental 4-cylinder 4-6-2 locomotives were ordered for operation on the North Western Railway. These were built at The Vulcan Foundry in 1930 and were all provided with camshaft operated poppet valves and large boilers with wide round-topped firebox and a working pressure of 225 lb.

The leading dimensions of all four locomotives are identical, but the X S1 are fitted with Caprotti valve gear whilst the XS2 have Lentz rotary cam valves. One engine of each type is designed with the inside and outside cranks arranged in the usual way (i.e., the inside are at 180° to the outside), but the second engine of each class has the inside cranks at 135° to the outside, thus producing eight beats per revolution of the driving wheels. The outside cylinders drive the second pair of coupled wheels and the inside cylinders drive on to the leading coupled axle.

All four engines are employed on express passenger duties between Peshawar and Lahore, and Lahore and Karachi, where they continue to do excellent work.

XS Class Locomotive hauling Express Train on the N.W. Railway

CHINESE NATIONAL RAILWAYS

4ft 8½in Gauge   **1935**   **4-8-4**

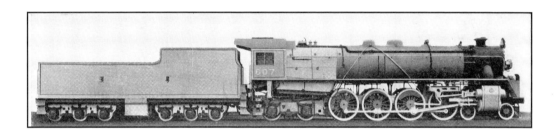

Cylinders	**(2) 20⅞ in. Diam. X 29½ in. Stroke**	Maximum Axleload		**16-8 tons**
Diameter Coupled Wheels	**5ft. 8⅞ in.**	Weight :		
		Engine in Working Order		**114-8 "**
Working Pressure	**220-5 lb.**	Tender „ „		**77 "**
Tractive Effort at 85% Pressure	**34,960 lb.**	Total „ „		**191-8 "**

The 4-8-4 locomotive illustrated above—one of 24 built for the Canton Hankow Railway in 1935—is of particular interest, especially as regards its size and dimensions.

Many unusual features were incorporated, and not the least of these is the booster engine with which six of them were equipped. This booster drives the rear axle of the leading bogie of the 12-wheeled tenders, but on the remaining 18 locomotives which were not fitted with this accessory when built, provision was made for it to be fitted to the trailing bogie of the engine at any time it might be required.

As will be seen from the dimensions, the boiler is of very large proportions with ample heating surface, 67 sq. ft. of grate area, and a wide round-topped steel firebox with four arch tubes, and combustion chamber for burning *ION* grade fuels. The ashpan has ash discharging doors. A tangential steam drier is located in the dome and coal is fed to the firebox by means of a B.K.1 type Standard stoker manufactured at Vulcan by arrangement with the Standard Stoker Company of U.S.A.

The superheated is also unusual and is of the Melesco E type with multiple - valve regulator header. It comprises 33 elements each of which occupies four flue tubes, with the exception of six which only occupy two. Superheated steam operates the stoker, booster, Westing-house air pump, turbogenerator, and chime whistle. A further special accessory is the cut-off control gauge which enables the driver to adjust the cut-off correctly for the most economical working of the engine, and also shows the steamchest pressure when coasting, and detects a leaky regulator or creeping reversing gear.

Front End View of 4-8-4 Locomotive Chinese National Railways

Bar frames are provided, the boiler being supported by the saddle casting under the smokebox and by sliding shoes and a breather plate at the front and rear of the firebox respectively. Additional breather plates are situated at appropriate points along the barrel.

The trailing bogie of the engine and both tender bogies are equipped with external Isothermos axleboxes and all coupled axleboxes and motion parts are grease lubricated.

Cylinders, steamchests, and smokebox saddle are cast integral in two halves and the cylinder barrels and piston valve liners are of nickel cast iron, the stroke being no less than 29½ in. with a travel of 9 in. for the 12⅝ in. diameter piston valves.

Air sanding is installed from a sand dome on the boiler top.

The large tender carried on two six-wheeled bogies, is of welded construction, and carries 11¾ tons of coal and 6,600 gallons of water.

Until 1932 the Canton Hankow Railway consisted of two unconnected stretches of line running due south from Hankow to Chuchow and from Lochang to Canton on

View of Interior of Cab, 4-8-4 Locomotive, Chinese National Railways

the seaboard. Traffic from Canton to Hankow and vice versa had to go by sea to Shanghai and then by a very roundabout rail route taking in all some 15 days.

In 1933 however, with the assistance of the Boxer Indemnity Fund, work was re-started on the 406 kms. of rocky and mountainous country connecting the two isolated links and this was completed in 1936, thereby enabling through name between Canton and Hankow to cover the distance in only 32 hours.

These large 4-8-4's ,were built to operate the new through traffic which at that time included the carriage of troops from South to North China to op- pose the Japanese. They were designed to negotiate curves of 150 metres radius and were required to deal with trains of 1,000 tons at 50 m.p.h. on the level, and 15 m.p.h. on the gradients of 1 in 66 which abound in this rugged country.

LONDON, MIDLAND & SCOTTISH RAILWAYS

4ft 8½in Gauge   **1936**   **2-8-0(8F)**

Cylinders	**(2) 18J in. Diam. x 28 in. Stroke**	Maximum Axleload	**16 tons (Tender 18 tons)**
Diameter Coupled Wheels	**4ft. 8½ in.**	Weight :	
		Engine in Working Order	**71-9** "
Working Pressure	**225 lb.**	Tender	**54** "
Tractive Effort at 85% Pressure	**32,440 lb.**	Total	**125-9** "

Sixty-nine of a powerful class of 2-8-0 freight locomotive, designated as Class 8F. were built by The Vulcan Foundry for the then London, Midland and Scottish Railway in 1936. These were to the designs of Sir William Stanier, were in accordance with the latest L.M.S. practice, and were required for the handling of heavy goods trains, in particular the coal traffic on the Midland Division between Toton and London.

The boiler is tapered, with a narrow Belpaire firebox and copper inner shell, and is pressed at 225 lb. per sq. in., the superheater having 21 elements.

Lubrication is mechanical by two Silvertown mechanical lubricators and all the engines are provided with exhaust steam injectors on the fireman's side.

The tenders are of six-wheel pattern with a capacity of 4,000 gallons of water and nine tons of coal and are fitted with water pick-up apparatus.

Class 8F Locomotive ascending Blea Moor Bank (L.M. Region)

At the beginning of the war this locomotive was selected by the Authorities, on account of its general capabilities, to be the first prototype for W.D. purposes and considerable numbers were built both by the Locomotive Industry and the British Railways.

Over 90 were sent to Iran in 1942 to operate on the extremely difficult Trans-Iranian Railway, and nearly all of these were converted to oil burning at Teheran Workshops by the Royal Engineers. A considerable number were also loaned and subsequently sold to the Egyptian Republic Railways where they took over the heaviest freight duties and also operated the Western Desert Line. Others are still at work in Palestine, Turkey and Italy, and in point of fact there is probably no other locomotive working to-day which has been built by so many different manufacturers and is operating in such a variety of different countries and climatic conditions.

INDIAN RAILWAYS

5ft 6in Gauge	1942	0-6-2 T (WW)

Cylinders	(2) 16 in. Diam. X 22 in. Stroke	Maximum Axleload		16-5 tons
Diameter Coupled Wheels	4 ft. 3 in.	Weight :		
Working Pressure	210 lb.	Engine in Working Order		65-85 "
Tractive Effort at 85% Pressure	19,710 lb.			

Just before World War II the Indian Railway Board placed orders with The Vulcan Foundry for four new types of tank locomotive of the various W series.

The smallest of these was the 0-6-2 WW Class for shunting duties in large stations and marshalling yards, four of which were completed in 1942.

Built to negotiate curves of 573 ft. radius and with a maximum permissive axleload of 16-5 tons, saving in weight by welding was employed wherever possible and the hopper ashpan, cab, tanks, bunker, smokebox saddle, and frame stretchers were all fabricated. The edges of the platform plates were also folded.

The boiler has a steel Belpaire firebox with flexible stays in the breaking zones, and the superheater has an MLS multiple-valve regulator header. The rocking and drop grates are both hand operated.

W.W. Locomotive shunting in Delhi Yard

The cylinders have liners of heat treated Meehanite "A" castings, and all motion pins are provided with Hoffmann needle roller-bearings with soft grease lubrication. The eccentric rod return-crank bushes are also grease lubricated and have Skefko spherical roller-bearings. Coupling rods and connecting rod big ends are provided with bronze floating bushes and are lubricated with hard grease.

All axleboxes are oil lubricated, but provision was made for the possible application of roller-bearings at a later date.

Standard Indian Government boiler mountings and accessories were employed throughout on all the W series locomotives.

These four engines were originally allocated to the North Western Railway, but since Partition they have been taken over by what is now the Northern Railway of India and employed in Delhi station and yard.

MINISTRY OF SUPPLY
(War Department)

4ft 8½in Gauge   **1943-45**   **2-8-0 (Austerity)**

Cylinders	**(2) 19 in. Diam. X 28 in. Stroke**	Maximum Axleload		**15-4 tons**
Diameter Coupled Wheels	**4ft. 8½ in.**	Weight :		
		Engine in Working Order		**69-8 "**
Working Pressure	**225 lb.**	Tender	" "	**55.85 "**
Tractive Effort at 85% Pressure	**34,215 lb.**	Total	" "	**25-65 "**

The first " Austerity " locomotive in a series of orders placed with The Vulcan Foundry by the Ministry of Supply on behalf of the War Department, to the general designs of Mr. R. A. Riddles, C.B.E., and comprising no less than 390 engines and tenders, was delivered in May 1943. The exigencies of war, both as regards our overseas lines of communication and the necessity for increasing the motive power available on the British Railways, made it essential to produce a simple, robust freight locomotive capable of sustained trouble-free service. At that time great care had to be taken regarding availability of materials and simplicity of manufacture, and although outwardly the appearance conformed to the customary standards adopted in this country and the majority of the economy measures adopted were not easily apparent, yet these latter were in fact substantial.

Especially was the use of steel castings and forgings eliminated wherever possible, due to the heavy requirements of these items by other war industries; fabricated parts were incorporated in lieu. Good examples of this principle are the axlebox guides which were made from flanged plate reinforced by triangular ribs, the brake hanger and spring link brackets which were of strip material, and the reversing rod and reversing shaft which were tubular with welded ends.

2-8-0 Austerity locomotives at Nijmegen, Holland

Another innovation was the use of cast iron for the coupled wheel centres.

The straightforward design of parallel boiler with round-topped firebox and very simple clothing arrangements made it particularly suitable for quantity production, and in fact all previous production records were broken in the building of these engines, no less than 206 being built at Vulcan in 1944.

The accessories, all of well-known make, included both vacuum and air brake equipment so that the locomotives might operate in any country and on any system.

Large numbers of these engines worked on the British Railways, assisting in the transport of the vast quantities of supplies to be moved before the invasion of Normandy. Subsequently they were all transferred to France, Holland, and Belgium where they were the mainstay of the Transportation effort during operations.

After the war a few of them remained in Holland, but the vast majority were returned to this country where they are now operating normal freight services on the Eastern Region of British Railways.

INDIAN RAILWAYS

5ft 6in Gauge   **1945**   **2-8-2 (XE)**

Cylinders	**(2) 23½ in. Diam. X 30 in. Stroke**	Maximum Axleload		**22-3 tons**
Diameter Coupled Wheels	**5ft. 1½ in.**	Weight :—		
Working Pressure	**210 lb.**	Engine in Working Order	**119-1** "
		Tender „ „	**77-3** "
Tractive Effort at *85%* Pressure	**48,086 lb.**	Total „ „	**196-4** "

The largest of the earlier Indian Standard broad gauge freight locomotives is the powerful 2-8-2 type known as the XE. In all, 51 of these were built at The Vulcan Foundry, and 35 of them constituted the first export contract to be handled after World War II.

Whilst the basic design follows that of the other contemporary standard types, the large dimensions of these machines are worthy of note, since they are the most powerful engines operating in India and the largest yet built by The Vulcan Foundry.

The boiler, with four arch tubes and wide round-topped firebox with combustion chamber, has a working pressure of 210 Ib., a grate area of 60 sq. ft., and an evaporative heating surface of 3,014 sq. ft., whilst the superheater has 36 elements.

An XE Boiler compared with one for a small locomotive

Two cylinders of 23½ in. diameter and coupled wheels 5ft. 1½ in. across the treads combine to give a tractive effort of 48,086 lb. at 85% pressure.

The 35 units delivered in 1945 differed from their predecessors inasmuch as they had re-designed cylinders and steam chests giving improved valve events, grease lubrication on side rods, big ends fitted with Skefko roller-bearings, and a Cole pattern hind truck.

The double bogie tender carries 6,000 gallons of water and 14 tons of coal.

LUXEMBURG RAILWAYS
AND U.N.R.R.A

4ft 8½in Gauge   **1946**   **2-8-0 (Liberation)**

Cylinders	**(2) 21⅝ in. Diam. X 28 in. Stroke**	Maximum Axleload		**18-5 tons**
Diameter Coupled Wheels	**4ft. 9⅛.in.**	Weight :		
		Engine in Working Order		**84-35 "**
Working Pressure	**227 lb.**	Tender	"	"
Tractive Effort at 85% Pressure	**43,800 lb.**	Total	"	"	**142-55 "**

The " Liberation " 2-8-0 Locomotive illustrated above is an unusually interest-ing machine, and 110 of them were supplied to U.N.R.R.A. immediately after World War II for use in Yugoslavia, Poland, and Czechoslovakia, a further 10 being delivered to Luxemburg.

The design owed its initiation to the Technical Advisory Committee on In-land Transport (T.A.C.I.T.) in collaboration with The Vulcan Foundry, the for-mer body consisting of members of the British and Allied Governments charged with the post-war reorganisation of Continental communications. Af-ter agreement as to the general specification to be adopted, T.A.C.I.T. re-quested the Ministry of Supply to place an order and The Vulcan Foundry were asked to work out the details and were given a very free hand in the matter. This, together with the co-operation of the Continental engineers, resulted in the production of a locomotive embodying many of the best features of British, Continental, and American practices.

Built to conform to the Berne loading gauge, the " Liberation " has a tractive effort of 43,800 Ib. at 85% pressure, a maximum axle load of 18-5 tons, and will negotiate curves of 330 ft. radius.

Difficulty regarding post-war lack of repair facilities on the Continent was catered for by simplicity of design and ease of maintenance, and with the

exception of proprietary fittings all details were designed to metric dimensions and all replaceable machine parts were manufactured to the International Standards Association system of tolerances to ensure interchangeability.

Continental Type Washout Door

The ample boiler, presses at 227lb, and having 44 sq.ft. of grate area, is provided with a round-topped firebox with copper inner shell and three arch tubes; it is radially stayed and is provided with flexible stays in the breaking zones. The boiler washout doors are of German type, the door having a flat face enclosed within a circular housing welded to the boiler, enabling all doors to be identical irrespective of their location. The superheater has 36 elements with a maximum steam temperature of 700°F.

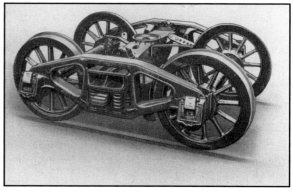

Cast Steel Plankless Tender Bogie

The circular smokebox, with door secured by dogs, rests on a cast iron saddle, and the cast steel frame stay below it carries the truck compensating beam bracket.

The ashpan is of the double hopper pattern and the firegrate is of the rocking type, the firebars being in the form of loose fingers carried on the rocking bars.

The Continental engineers required rhomboidal steam ports and in consequence the piston valves have the unusually large diameter of 12 in. The Walschaert valve gear is of simple design and has no offsets, and an unusual feature is the crosshead arm attachment which is by means of a tapered pin pressed into the crosshead and secured by a cotter.

It was impossible at that time to obtain steel slabs for bar frames and therefore plate frames were provided conforming to normal British practice.

All lubrication except at a few minor points is by oil, fed from Wakefield mechanical lubricators.

The tender has tank and bunker of all-welded construction and is provided with two four-wheeled American pattern cast steel bogies of the plankless type. These consist virtually of only three pieces, two side frames and one cross bolster, resulting in considerable saving in weight and facility of assembly.

Other points of interest include two Everlasting blowdown cocks, reflex water gauges, forged steel manifold, two Davies & Metcalfe 12 mm. lifting and restarting hot water injectors of special design for operation in Eastern Europe under winter conditions, compressed air sanding apparatus with the sandbox on the boiler top, overhead springing compensated in two groups, a powerful Westinghouse cross compound air compressor for dealing with very heavy fully fitted freight trains, and very complete electric lighting equipment.

The " Liberations" in service in Yugoslavia are employed between Belgrade and Divaça and between the port of Susak on the Adriatic Sea and Moraviçe. Trains of 360 tons are regularly handled on this latter section where long winding gradients of 2.5% abound.

10 "Liberation" Locomotives in steam in Luxemburg Running Shed

The 15 locomotives sent to Czechoslovakia are stationed at Ceska Trebova, 102 miles east of Prague, and from this centre they work freight trains of 1,200-1,300 tons to Prague, Brno, and Olamuec, with ruling gradients of 1 in 125.

The 10 Luxemburg engines are used not only on freight trains but also for general passenger work including the Paris-Liege expresses.

In all the countries where these locomotives are employed their free steaming and economical coal consumption have been the subject of particular comment.

BURMA RAILWAYS

Metre Gauge	1947	2-6-2 (YB)

Cylinders	**(2) 16 in. Diam. X 24 in. Stroke**	Maximum Axleload		**10 tons**
Diameter Coupled Wheels	**4 ft. 9 in.**	Weight :		
		Engine in Working Order		**51-75 "**
Working Pressure	**180 lb.**	Tender " "		**39.25 "**
Tractive Effort at 85% Pressure	**16,492 lb**	Total " "		**91 "**

The YB 4-6-2 passenger locomotive has been a standard type on the metre gauge lines of the Indian Railways for many years and considerable numbers have been supplied from time to time by The Vulcan Foundry.

During World War II the robust qualities of the YB also became popular in Burma and as that country had a large proportion of its locomotive stock destroyed during hostilities, 50 of these engines, modernised and brought up to date, were subsequently ordered from Vulcan and shipped to Rangoon in 1947 to assist in overcoming this situation.

Destined for service on passenger and mixed trains, their 10 ton axle load enables them to work on any line on the Burma Railway except for one short stretch south of Moulmein.

The boiler with wide type Belpaire firebox and steel inner shell, combustion chamber, and three arch tubes, has the tubes arranged in vertical banking. It is also equipped with Continental type washout doors of standard size, capable of being used anywhere on the boiler irrespective of position.

The axles of the tender, engine bogie, and hind truck are all equipped with Timken roller-bearings, whilst the eccentric rod big ends also revolve on roller-bearings, these latter being by Skefko Ltd. The cylinder diameter is 16 in. and that of the coupled wheels 4 ft. 9 in., whilst all other wheels on both engine and tender have a uniform diameter of 2 ft. 4½ in.

The coupled axleboxes are lubricated by grease on the Ajax system and hard grease is also applied to the rods. The motion is oil lubricated and a Wakefield sight-feed lubricator with transfer filler feeds the valves and pistons.

A radial-arm spring-con trolled hind truck takes the place of the Cartazzi slides and radial axleboxes fitted to earlier engines of this type.

A tubular reversing rod is provided and the union link connection to the crosshead consists of a tapered pin driven into the latter and secured with a cotter.

Other features include a dumper ashpan, hand-operated finger bar type rocking and drop grate, Stone's electric lighting, one No. 9 Gresham & Craven live steam injector and one No. 7 Davies &

View of Cab of YB Locomotive

Metcalfe exhaust steam injector, Parry soot blower, the Vacuum Brake Co.'s brake equipment, and a Stone's electrical speed indicator driven off a spigot on the right trailing crankpin to assist drivers to observe speed restrictions.

Cab, 3,000 gallon water tank, and bunker are of all-welded construction and the coal capacity of eight tons is greater than that of any previous YB tender.

YB Locomotive in steam in Rangoon Yard

These locomotives were all finish painted in dark olive green with stainless steel clothing bands and orange lettering, and were among the first British exports to arrive in Burma after that country became an independent republic.

TURKISH STATE RAILWAYS

4ft 8½in Gauge   **1948**   **2-10-0 (IE)**

Cylinders	**(2) 25⅝in. Diam. X 26 in. Stroke**	Maximum Axleload		**18-7 tons**
Diameter Coupled Wheels	**4ft. 9⅛ in.**	Weight :		
Working Pressure	**227 lb.**	Engine in Working Order		**106-9 "**
		Tender "	"	**60.8 "**
Tractive Effort at 85% Pressure	**57,560 lb.**	Total "	"	**167.7 "**

In 1939 a contract was placed in this country by the Turkish State Railways (T.C.D.D.) for a number of Class 1E freight locomotives of a previous German design, but due to the intervention of the war, the order could not be completed until 1948. Twenty-two of these engines were built at Vulcan for operation on the difficult and mountainous main lines in Asia Minor radiating from Ankara and Eskisehir. These exceptionally powerful locomotives have a tractive effort at 85% pressure of 57,560 lb., and a maximum axleload of 18-7 tons.

The boiler, with an evaporative heating surface of 2,575 sq. ft., has a very long barrel with round-topped firebox, the inner firebox and water stays being of copper. The superheater has 43 elements and the header is cast in two parts to separate the saturated and superheated chambers, whilst the two domes house a water purifier and a Wagner regulator respectively.

A three hopper ashpan is fitted, with three sets of fixed bars and a section to form a drop grate.

2-10-0 Locomotive for Turkey en-route to the Docks

The bar frames are 3½ in. thick and have a cast steel stay between the cylinders and a fabricated smokebox saddle, and the spring gear is compensated in two groups. The coupled axleboxes are of forged steel with brasses lined with white metal, the keeps being equipped with Armstrong oilers.

The connecting and coupling rods are all provided with adjustable bushes, and due to the long coupled wheelbase of 24 ft. 11 in. special provision for lateral play has been made by the use of spherical bearings in the leading and trailing rods.

The Westinghouse straight air and automatic brake equipment is fed from a 7 in. cross compound air compressor, and an interesting feature is the inclusion of Riggenbach counter pressure brake equipment for operation on long down grades with the engine in reverse gear. This is operated by a slide valve in the exhaust pipe worked from an air cylinder in the cab, which then allows the cylinders to function as compressors.

Lubrication of the locomotive is by oil throughout, and a Wakefield mechanical lubricator and sight-feed indicator supplies 14 feeds to the valves, pistons, piston rods, valve rods, and tailrods. The leading truck is of the Krauss type in which the truck wheels are connected to the leading coupled axle by an arm with controlled side movement.

The cab is of German State Railways standard design, and other features include two Clyde soot blowers, a Marcotty firedoor, Teloc speed indicator, Alfol insulation, Everlasting blow-off cock, air-operated sanders with sandbox on the boiler top, one Davies & Metcalfe No. 11 exhaust steam injector and one No. 11 live steam injector.

The relatively small tender, carried on two diamond framed bogies, has a welded tank and a capacity of 6,380 gallons of water and 7¾ tons of coal. The locomotives were finish painted in black with chromium bands and vermilion wheel centres, and were put on rail at Haidar Pasha.

NIGERIAN RAILWAYS

3ft 6in Gauge   **1948**   **2-8-2 (River)**

Cylinders	**(2) 18 in. Diam. X 26 in. Stroke**	Maximum Axleload	**13**	**tons**
Diameter Coupled Wheels	**4ft. 0 in.**	Weight:		
Working Pressure	**200lb**	Engine in Working Order	**71.5**	**"**
		Tender " "	**47.5**	**"**
Tractive Effort at 85% Pressure	**29,800 lb**	Total " "	**119**	**"**

In 1948 20 2-8-2 freight locomotives of new type and known as the "River" class, were designed and built at Newton-le-Willows for the Nigerian Railway, where they were urgently required for the rapidly increasing post-war traffic, including the transport of the large backlog of groundnuts which had then accumulated.

The boiler has a wide all-steel Belpaire firebox with Hulson type grate 38 sq. ft. in area, suitable for the low calorific value of Nigerian coal (11,350 B.T. U's), and three arch tubes.

The ashpan is of the single hopper type and the smokebox is fitted with self-cleaning plates, whilst the washout doors fit on flat seatings welded to the barrel and are thus all interchangeable.

Bar frames 4 in. thick are provided, together with overhung springs without compensation.

The coupled axleboxes are of cast steel with phosphor bronze bearings and whitemetal inserts. Both leading and trailing engine trucks are of the radial arm type with outside roller-bearing axleboxes of Skefko manufacture interchangeable with those of the double bogie tender.

"River" Class Locomotive on down Plateau Limited at Jebba Station

The connecting rod big ends and the coupling rods have floating phosphor bronze bushes and lubrication is by oil throughout.

Two steam turrets are provided, one between the chimney and the dome and the other on the firebox top outside the cab.

The locomotive is provided with a steam brake together with vacuum equipment for controlling the train, the latter being specially designed to the requirements of the Crown Agents by the Vacuum Brake Co., with the ejector outside the cab, thus minimising the heat for the driver as far as possible.

The tender tank is of welded construction and carries 4,000 gallons of water, whilst the coal capacity is 10 tons.

Since 1948 many more of the same class have been built and the design has served as a basis for locomotives in Nyasaland and also the metre gauge lines of East Africa.

In 1954 Vulcan completed a further 15 engines for Nigeria with various modifications introduced in the light of experience gained in service.

These modifications include continuous main frames throughout the length of the engine, compensation for the spring gear in two groups, Skefko roller-bearing axleboxes on the coupled wheels, multiple valve regulator, bye-pass valves on the steamchests, and sandboxes on top of the boiler. The tender sideplates above the water tank have also been dispensed with in these later locomotives.

ARGENTINE RAILWAYS
(General Roca Railway)

Cylinders	**(2) 19J in. Diam. x 28 in. Stroke**	Maximum Axleload		**15·6 tons**
Diameter Coupled Wheels	**5ft. 8in**	Weight:		
		Engine in Working Order	**82·35**	"
Working Pressure	**225 lb.**	Tender	**66.1**	"
Tractive Effort at 85% Pressure	**29,943 lb.**	Total	**148·45**	"

Just prior to the nationalisation of the Argentine Railways, the then Buenos AiresGreat Southern Railway placed an order with Vulcan for 30 4-8-0 mixed traffic locomotives to be known as Class 15B.

These engines were delivered in 1949 and were a development of the eight 15A Class built earlier at Vulcan in 1938, which in turn were based on the original Buenos Aires Western Railway 1500 design.

The boiler, which has a 27 element superheater, is provided with a Belpaire firebox with sloping top and tapered sides and a steel inner shell. Oil fuel is the firing medium controlled by means of the railway's own combined apparatus which synchronises the correct opening of oil valve, atomiser, blower, and damper for any position of the regulator.

Plate frames are fitted, the coupled springs being of the underslung type, compensated throughout.

The 19½ in. diameter cylinders are provided with extra large area steam ports and have a stroke of 28 in.

The engine bogie is of the swing link type with inside bearings, in contrast to the external axlebox arrangement on the 15A Class.

Connecting and coupling rods are grease lubricated. Accessories include a Gresham & Craven No. 10 live steam injector, a Davies & Metcalfe No. 9 exhaust steam injector, Detroit sight-feed lubricator, continuous blow-down valve, and steam-operated cylinder draincocks.

15B Locomotive passing Sierra de la Ventana with Express Fruit Train

The tender, carrying 6,000 gallons of water and 11-6 tons of oil fuel, is of welded construction and the double plate tender bogies are carried on Skefko roller-bearing axleboxes.

The relatively light axleload of 15-6 tons enables these powerful locomotives to operate on a large number of lines and services. Originally intended for hauling 1,000 ton express fruit trains between the Rio Negro valley and Buenos Aires, their use has been extended to both express passenger and sleeping car trains between the Capital and Bahia Blanca, and also to operation on the late Patagonian State Railway which runs West to the tourist centre of San Carlos de Bariloche in the Argentine Lake District.

ARGENTINE RAILWAYS

5ft 6in Gauge   **1950 and 1953**   **4-6-2 (PS.11)**

Cylinders	**(3) 19i in. Diam. X 26 in. Stroke**	Maximum Axleload	**18 tons**
Diameter Coupled Wheels	**6ft. 2½in.**	Weight:	
		Engine in Working Order	**99-7 "**
Working Pressure	**225 lb.**	Tender	**102 "**
Tractive Effort at 85% Pressure	**38,068lb.**	Total	**201-7 "**

The original PS. 11 4-6-2 Pacific was the standard express passenger locomotive of the late Central Argentine Railway, now the Bartolomé Mitre Railway. So successful was it that upon nationalisation of the Argentine Railways, the Authorities decided to standardise this class for express passenger service on three railways, the Roca, the Bartolomé Mitre, and the San Martin, where very heavy trains and continuous high speeds are a daily occurrence, and in consequence an order for 50 additional units, duly modified and modernised, was placed with The Vulcan Foundry.

As a result these locomotives—among the most powerful in the world on a power for adhesive weight basis—are operating express trains of up to 750 tons weight on all three above-mentioned railways, including the seaside expresses between Buenos Aires and Mar del Plata, the " Cuyano " and " Internacional " between Buenos Aires and Mendoza en route for Chile, the sleeping car traffic from the Cordoba hills, and the business expresses between Buenos Aires and Rosario.

One of the original locomotives created a South American speed record in 1939 by averaging 65-7 m.p.h. with 500 tons on the non-stop run of 188 miles between Rosario and Buenos Aires, during which a maximum speed of nearly 100 m.p.h. was attained. The engines have a tractive effort at 85% pressure of 38,068 lb., and are of the three-cylinder simple type. They are oil fired and are equipped with British-Caprotti rotary cam poppet valve gear, and double six-wheel bogie tenders.

The large boiler, with 2,208 sq. ft. of evaporative heating surface and grate area of 43 sq. ft., has a wide round-topped firebox with steel inner shell, the throat and backplates being welded to the wrapper and the tubeplate riveted. Plate frames are provided and the cylinders are of cast steel with nickel alloy iron liners in the barrels. The crank axle is of the built-up type, and the connecting and coupling rods are of Vibrac steel, arranged for grease lubrication.

P.S. 11 Locomotive with Express Passenger Train on the General Roca Railway

Compensation is provided between all the underslung coupled springs, and the cast steel coupled axleboxes with bronze bearings are oil lubricated.

The Caprotti valve gear is of the latest type with valves actuated by steam pressure.

The leading bogie has spring side control and the hind truck is provided with radial axleboxes.

Accessories include a Davies & Metcalfe H.J. exhaust steam injector, a No. 11 live steam injector, Clyde sandgun, water gauges with prismatic indicator glasses, Detroit sight-feed lubricator, Teloc speed indicator, Stone's electric lighting, and steam brake for engine and tender in conjunction with vacuum equipment for the train brakes.

The tenders are the largest ever built at Vulcan and in fact, when fully loaded, their weight is greater than that of the engine. The two six-wheeled Commonwealth bogies are of the swing bolster type, both frames and bolsters being of cast steel.

Both water and fuel tanks are all-welded; in some cases the capacities are 9,000 gallons of water and 11-6 tons of oil fuel respectively, and in others 10,000 gallons and eight tons, this being according to the particular services for which they were destined.

GOLD COAST RAILWAYS

| 3ft 6in Gauge | 1951 | 4-8-2 (248Class) |

Cylinders	**(2) 18 in. Diam. X 24 in. Stroke**	Maximum Axleload	**12-5**	**tons**
Diameter Coupled Wheels	**4 ft. 0 in.**	Weight:		
		Engine in Working Order	**68-5**	**"**
Working Pressure	**200 lb.**	Tender " "	**43-9**	**"**
Tractive Effort at 85% Pressure	**27,540lb.**	Total	**112-4**	**"**

In 1951 30 4-8-2 freight locomotives were built and supplied to the 3 ft. 6 in. gauge Gold Coast Railway. These were similar in many ways to an earlier series also built at Vulcan Foundry in 1939.

The boiler has a wide round-topped firebox with copper inner shell and the working pressure is 200 Ib., a 4 in. Lockyer regulator being located in the dome.

41

Loco. No. 249 on Passenger Train, Gold Coast Railway

An all-welded hopper ashpan, Hulson type grate, and self-cleaner plates in the smokebox, are provided and the superheater has 18 elements.

The engine has bar frames and overhead springing, compensated in two groups, each cylinder being cast integral with half the smokebox saddle.
A particularly interesting detail is that all the axleboxes of both engine and tender, including those of the coupled wheels, are equipped with Timken roller-bearings, and all the wheel centres are of the S.C.O.A.-P. type.

All coupling and connecting rods also revolve on roller-bearings.

The all-welded tenders are larger than those of the earlier series and carry $7\frac{1}{2}$ tons of coal and 4,000 gallons of water.

These locomotives have many features in common with 10 also built at Newton-le-Willows earlier in the same year for freight work on the Tasmanian Government Railways.

INDIAN RAILWAYS

5ft 6in Gauge 1951 **2-8-2 (WG)**

Cylinders	**(2) 21 in. Diam. x 28 in. Stroke**	Maximum Axleload	**18.5 tons**
Diameter Coupled Wheels	**5ft. 1½ in.**	Weight:	
		Engine in Working Order	**101-85** "
Working Pressure	**210 lb.**	Tender " "	**71-8** "
Tractive Effort at 85% Pressure	**38,890 lb.**	Total	**173-65** "

The 2-8-2 WG is the post-war Indian Standard broad gauge freight locomotive constructed to the requirements of the Central Standards Office at New Delhi, and 10 of these were produced at Newton-le-Willows in 1951.

The tractive effort of the WG—38,890 lb. at 85% pressure—lies between that of the XE and the XD, but since its maximum axleload is only 18½ tons, it has a very wide service range over the Indian main lines. Many of the details, including the boiler, motion, springs, axleboxes, and hind truck, are all interchangeable with those of the 4-6-2 WP passenger engines built in the U.S.A.

The boiler barrel consists of three rings, the centre one being coned, and the wide round-topped firebox, with all-welded steel inner shell, has one Nicholson thermic syphon and two arch tubes. A Joco regulator is fitted in the dome and the Melesco superheater has 38 elements. The hand-operated rocking grate is in four sections, and the welded ashpan, in two parts, is of the double hopper type.

Bar type main frames are provided together with a rear frame consisting of a one-piece cast steel cradle. The frame pedestal wedges and shoes are of forged steel fitted with renewable manganese steel liners.

The lead bronze coupled axleboxes have Ajax keeps with grease lubricators and the overhung spring gear is compensated in two groups. Both leading and trailing trucks are fitted with Skefko roller-bearing axleboxes, the former being of the cannon type and the latter with outside bearings. Disc wheel centres are provided on both trucks. The cylinders are of cast steel with cast iron liners and each one is made integral with half the smokebox saddle.

The connecting and coupling rods are provided with bronze floating bushes and hard grease lubrication, but the motion is fitted with cast iron bushes lubricated by soft grease. The eccentric rods revolve on roller-bearings.

Accessories include two I.R.S. 12 mm. injectors, three 3 in. Ross Pop safety valves, two Everlasting blow off cocks, a five-feed Wakefield A.C. lubricator, and Stone's electric lighting. Steam actuates the engine brake, vacuum equipment being provided for the tender and train brakes. The large capacity sandbox is mounted on top of the boiler barrel.

The tender, which has a capacity of 5,000 gallons of water and 18 tons of coal, has provision for the fitting of a mechanical stoker should this be required at a later date.

The tender bogie frames are of cast steel and Skefko roller-bearing axleboxes are provided, the wheels being of the disc type as on the engine trucks.

Large numbers of these WG locomotives are now in service all over India.

EGYPTIAN REPUBLIC RAILWAYS

4ft 8½in Gauge   **1952**   **2-8-0 (700 Class)**

Cylinders	**(2) 18i in. Diam. X 28 in. Stroke**	Maximum Axleload		**16.5 tons**
Diameter Coupled Wheels	**4ft. 8½in.**	Weight :		
		Engine in Working Order		**75.6** "
Working Pressure	**225 lb.**	Tender	"	"	**70.6** "
Tractive Effort at 85% Pressure	**32,450 lb.**	Total	"	"	**146-2** "

As mentioned earlier in this book, a substantial number of L.M.S. Class 8F 2-8-0 loco-motives which were converted to oil-burning and used in Egypt during World War II, were later purchased by the Egyptian Republic Railways.

This type proved very satisfactory on freight duties and as a result the Egyptian Authorities subsequently placed orders for considerable numbers of additional loco-motives suitably modified to meet Egyptian conditions. The Vulcan Foundry partici-pated in these orders and delivered 20 of these engines to Alexandria in 1952.

Instead of the tapered boiler of the L.M.S. engines, the boiler in this case is parallel and the Belpaire firebox has an all-welded steel inner shell provided with one Nich-olson thermic syphon. Since oil fuel is the firing medium, a shallow welded firepan is fitted which can be removed without lifting the boiler.

The superheater has 21 elements and the return bends of these were left 4 ft. 5 in. from the firebox tubeplate. A Joco regulator and a steam drier are provided in the dome.

The plate frames are 1⅛ in. thick and continuous hornblocks are fitted at all coupled axlebox openings, the axleboxes themselves being of Stone's bronze, lubricated by hard grease blocks on the Ajax system. Manganese steel liners are provided on both boxes and guides. The springing is underhung without compensation.

The tender water tank is of welded and riveted construction and has a capacity of 5,500 gallons, but the oil tank is welded throughout and carries 9-6 tons of fuel thus enabling the locomotives to remain in traffic for extended periods.

The two four-wheeled tender bogies are fitted with Timken roller-bearing axleboxes.

These robust freight locomotives are stationed at Boulaq el Dakrour (Cairo), Gabbary (Alexandria), and Minia in Upper Egypt, and operate goods trains on all the principal main lines.

2-8-0 Locomotives for Egypt loaded on board prior to sailing

INDIAN RAILWAYS

5ft 6in Gauge   **1952**   **2-6-4 T (WM)**

Cylinders	**(2) 16 in. Diam. X 28 in. Stroke**	Maximum Axleload	**16-25 tons**
Diameter Coupled Wheels	**5 ft. 7 in.**	Weight :	
Working Pressure	**210 lb**	Engine in Working Order	**96-6 "**
Tractive Effort at 85° Pressure	**19,100 lb.**		

In the late 1930's the Indian Railway Board placed orders with Vulcan for a number of new type Standard tank locomotives designated as the W series and 10 of these were of the 2-6-4 T WM Class, destined for use on the then G.I.P. and E.I. Railways, and delivered in 1942.

In 1952 30 more of these engines, with only slight modifications, were built at Vulcan, and these are all in operation on the heavy suburban work of the Eastern Railway from Calcutta.

A WM Locomotive With Suburban Train at Bandel Station, E. Ry.

The boiler has a Belpaire firebox, and the all-welded steel inner shell is provided with two arch tubes. The superheater is of AX pattern with 21 A-type elements.

The grate comprises a dump bar at the front with hand operated rocking bars in two sections, provision being made for fitting a rocking grate cylinder at a later date if necessary. The ashpan is of the single hopper type in two parts, so arranged that air openings are provided on all four sides, air control doors being dispensed with.

The overhead spring gear for the coupled and front truck wheels is compensated throughout and the journals of the bronze coupled axleboxes are hard grease lubricated; the coupled wheel centres are of the S.C.O.A.-P. type.

The big ends and coupling rod bearings are also lubricated with hard grease, but the gudgeon pins and knuckle pins are arranged for soft grease.

The radial arm front truck has a Timken cannon type roller-bearing axlebox and the outside journals of the trailing bogie are also provided with Timken roller-bearings.

The two side tanks, bunker tank and middle tank under the boiler, all of welded construction, provide a water capacity of 3,000 gallons, whilst the coal bunker carries 6-5 tons.

Accessories include a Joco regulator, two Gresham & Craven No. 8 live steam injectors, two Everlasting blowdown cocks, a continuous blowdown valve, Wakefield A.C. sight-feed lubricator, and Stone's electric lighting.

IRANIAN STATE RAILWAYS

4ft 8½in Gauge   **1952-53**   **2-10-2 (52)**

Cylinders	**(2) 24-01 in. Diam. X 26 in. Stroke**	Maximum Axleload		**16-75 tons**
Diameter Coupled Wheels	**4 ft. 3 in.**	Weight :		
		Engine in Working Order		**108-5 "**
Working Pressure	**199 lb.**	Tender	" "	**67.3 "**
Tractive Effort at 85%. Pressure	**49,800 lb.**	Total	" "	**175-8 "**

The 2-10-2 freight locomotive illustrated above, one of 64 built in 1952 and 1953 for the Iranian State Railways, is an entirely new design and is one of the most powerful engines ever sent to the Middle East.

*2-10-2
Locomotives
Being
Steamed
At Bandar
Shahpur*

The Trans-Iranian Railway, connecting Bandar Shahpur on the Persian Gulf with Teheran, the capital, and Bandar Shah on the Caspian Sea, is one of the world's greatest railway engineering achievements, and these locomotives have to stand up to operating conditions perhaps unequalled in their difficulty.

On the Southern plain temperatures of 140°F. in the shade are encountered, but in the North the winter conditions are most rigorous. From Andimeshk to Doroud, a distance of 208 kms. over the Elvend Mountains, there are innumerable tunnels and almost continuous gradients of 1-5% with curves and reverse curves as sharp at 180 metres radius. The specification laid it down that a speed of 25 k.p.h. should be maintained with trains of 600 tons on this section, and this condition was fulfilled with ease.

North of Teheran the railway rises to a height of over 7,000 ft. when crossing the Elburz range and here the terrain is even stiffer, and includes a section 66 kms. long of continuous 2-8% gradient over which trains of 300 tons have to be handled in all weathers.

Built entirely to metric dimensions and arranged for oil firing, these engines have a tractive effort of 49,800 lb. at 85% pressure and are provided with large boilers having a total evaporative heating surface of 2,731-2 sq. ft.

One of The Boilers in course of construction

*View inside
The Cab of one
Of the 2-10-2
Locomotives*

*2-10-2 Locomotives on board
ship at Liverpool*

The firebox is round-topped with a welded steel inner shell and the superheater has 36 elements. There are two domes, the front one housing tray and baffles for water purification, and the rear one an Owen's double beat regulator. The large capacity sandboxes are also located on top of the boiler.

The rolled steel bar frames are 110 mm. (4-33 in.) thick and extend the full length of the engine bed and are adequately stayed throughout by steel castings and fabricated vertical stretchers.

Forged steel pedestal guides are provided, fitted with renewable manganese steel liners which work against similar liners in the axleboxes; these latter are of cast steel with gunmetal bushes lined with white metal and they are provided with Armstrong oilers in the keeps.

The springing is of the overhead type compensated in two groups and each cylinder is cast integral with half the smokebox saddle.

The leading truck has a cannon type axlebox fitted with Timken roller-bearings and these are also applied to the outside-bearing axleboxes of the radial arm trailing truck. All the coupled wheel centres are of the S.C.O.A.-P. type.

Lubrication is by oil throughout and that of the valves and pistons is provided by a 12 feed Wakefield mechanical lubricator.

The Westinghouse brake equipment is fed by a powerful 7 in. cross compound air compressor mounted under the platform, and both driver's automatic and independent brake valves are provided. Other accessories include two Davies & Metcalfe live steam injectors, three Ross Pop safety valves, Klinger water gauges, three Williams type steam-operated blow-off cocks, steam-operated cylinder draincocks, air-operated sanding valves, Laycock steam-heating valve, Teloc speed recorder, and steam chest pressure gauge with pyrometer indicator.

Unloading a 2-10-2 Locomotive at Bandar Shahpur

The Stone's electric lighting equipment is exceptionally complete and, in addition to the usual head, tail, and other lights, a searchlight is provided on each side of the boiler for use at stations and on the curves in the mountains.

The tender tanks are of welded construction carried on an all-welded underframe and the water and oil fuel capacities are 6,600 gallons and 8-4 tons respectively. The two diamond-framed tender bogies are also fitted with Timken roller-bearing axleboxes.

The locomotives were all shipped in Messrs. Belships' vessels and unloaded at Bandar Shahpur jetty where in spite of a coupled wheelbase of 19 ft. 8¼ in. they were hauled round a 120 metre radius curve without difficulty.

IRAQI STATE RAILWAYS

Metre Gauge   **1953**   **2-8-2 (Y)**

Cylinders	**(2) 17 in. Diam. X 24 in. Stroke**	Maximum Axleload	**10 tons**	
Diameter Coupled Wheels	**4 ft. 0 in.**	Weight:		
		Engine in Working Order .	**56-35**	"
Working Pressure	**180 lb.**	Tender " "	**40-3**	"
Tractive Effort at 85% Pressure	**22.110lb.**	Total " "	**96-65**	"

The YD 2-8-2 has been a standard metre gauge freight locomotive on the Indian Railways for some time and Vulcan supplied a considerable number of these, and also built 20 for Burma in 1949.

The latest example of this engine however is illustrated above and is one of an order for 10, known as the Y Class, built for the Iraqi State Railways in 1953 for main line goods duties between Baghdad and Basra and Baghdad and Kirkuk, where the maximum axleload is restricted to 10 tons.

These locomotives are arranged for oil firing to the Iraqi State Railways standard requirements, the burners being of a modified Booth pattern. The boiler has a Belpaire firebox with a steel inner shell of riveted construction and is equipped with a Melesco superheater of 21 elements.

Lubrication of the valves and pistons is by Wakefield AC.2 sight-feed lubricator. The connecting rod little ends are lubricated by oil, but the big ends, coupling rods, and coupled axleboxes are all equipped for hard grease.

The leading and hind trucks are fitted with Timken roller-bearings, the former having cannon axleboxes; the eccentric cranks also revolve on roller-bearings and these latter are of Skefko manufacture.

The plate frames are 1in. thick and the spring gear is compensated in two groups, both engine and tender being fitted with A.B.C. centre couplers.

The large capacity sandbox is located on the boiler top.

The double-bogie tenders are also equipped with Timken roller-bearing axleboxes, identical with those on the engine trailing truck. Tender water capacity is 3,000 gallons and the fuel tank-carries 7.1 tons of oil.

The engines and tenders were shipped to Basra, mainly from Manchester Docks.

VICTORIAN GOVERNMENT RAILWAYS

5ft.3in. Gauge   **1954**   **2-8-0 (J)**

Cylinders	**(2) 20 in. Diam. X 26 in. Stroke**	Maximum Axleload		**14·75 tons**
Diameter Coupled Wheels	**4ft. 7in**	Weight:		
		Engine in Working Order	**67.75**	"
Working Pressure	**175 lb.**	Tender " "	**45.35**	"
Tractive Effort at 85% Pressure	**28,650 lb.**	Total " "	**113.1**	"

Immediately after World War II Victoria, in common with most of the other Australian States, turned its attention to making up arrears in the renewal of its motive power and rolling stock, and they included in this programme 60 2-8-0 J Class locomotives which were built by The Vulcan Foundry in 1954 to the designs and requirements of the Chief Mechanical Engineer of the Victorian Government Railways.

These relatively light freight locomotives, with a maximum axle load of only 14¾ tons, are a modified version of the K Class, and 30 of them are for coal burning whilst the remaining 30 are oil fired.

The boiler has a Belpaire firebox with a welded steel inner shell and two arch tubes, and it is fitted with a particularly large dome, housing a balanced regulator of the railway's own pattern.

The M.L.S. superheater has 21 elements and in the case of the oil fired engines their length has been reduced to give an increased distance between return bend and tubeplate—3 ft. 0 in.

The coal fired engines have a Hulson type grate and double hopper ashpan with sliding doors operated by an air cylinder, whilst those burning oil have a flamepan with air door and also short air tubes through the sloping side brick walls.

The frames are of 1 in. plate and the underhung springs are compensated in two groups, the oil lubricated coupled and front truck axleboxes being of cast steel with gunmetal bearings lined with whitemetal.

The coupled wheels all have cast steel S.C.O.A.-P. centres.

The cast iron cylinders contain pistons of built up type having forged steel centres and cast iron bull rings secured by rivets, tailrods also being provided. The piston valves are 10 in. in diameter and are of the Pennsylvania pattern. Lubrication of these components is by a six-feed Nathan mechanical lubricator.

The locomotives are equipped with Westinghouse air brake equipment fed by a 7 in. cross compound air pump on the side of the boiler.

General fittings include two Davies & Metcalfe No. 9 Nathan type understep injectors, two Coale type safety valves, Klinger water gauges, two blow-off cocks, Flaman speed indicator, Pyle National electric lighting, and air-operated sanding. The coal fired engines are also equipped with Ajax air-operated firedoors.

The plain-bearing double-bogie tenders have prefabricated welded under-frames and a capacity of 7 tons of coal and 4,200 gallons of water. In the case of the oil burning locomotives the water tank is slightly modified to accommodate an all-welded cylindrical oil fuel tank holding 6-8 tons of oil.

Full provision has been made to allow of the conversion of these locomotives from 5 ft. 3 in. to standard gauge should this be required in the future.

ANTOFAGASTA BOLIVIA RAILWAY

Metre Gauge	**1954**	**4-8-2**

Cylinders	**(2) 19 in. Diam. X 26 in. Stroke**	Maximum Axleload	**15**	**tons**
Diameter Coupled Wheels	**4 ft. 0 in.**	Weight :		
		Engine in Working Order	**88-1**	"
Working Pressure	**200 lb.**	Tender " "	**58.05**	"
Tractive Effort at 85% Pressure	**33,240 lb.**	Total " "	**146-15**	"

The Antofagasta Bolivia Railway connects the port of Antofagasta in Northern Chile with La Paz, the capital of Bolivia, situated on the High Plateau of that country. To do so it has to cross the Andes mountains and climb to a height of 13,396 ft., and virtually the whole of the Bolivian Section of the railway operates at an altitude of over 12,000 ft. In 1954, The Vulcan Foundry built 16 4-8-2 oil-burning locomotives for this railway, 6 for the Chilean Section and 10 for the Bolivian.

To ensure an adequate supply of steam on the continuous and arduous gradients, the locomotives are provided with a very large boiler consisting of a 3-course barrel and Belpaire firebox with all-welded steel inner shell.

The superheater has 28 elements and the regulator is of the multiple valve type with a shutdown valve in the dome.

Boiler mountings include a No. 12 Friedman live steam injector and a No. 11 HJ exhaust steam injector, top-feed clackboxes with feed trays, three Ross Pop safety valves, Klinger water gauges, and 2 Everlasting blow-off cocks.

The main slab frames are 4 in. thick and the cylinders are of cast iron, each being made integral with half the smokebox saddle.

The springs are compensated in two groups and all axleboxes are of cast steel with Stone's bronze and white metal bearings arranged for oil lubrication from a Wakefield mechanical lubricator, except on two locomotives where the coupled bearings are of plain bronze with Ajax grease lubricators.

The hind truck is of the Cole type with side spring control. On 14 engines the motion, connecting and coupling rods are lubricated by oil, but the remaining two are arranged for soft grease.

Other equipment includes Westinghouse air brakes, Henricot automatic couplers, Wakefield sight-feed lubricator, Walter's split bushes, Stone's electric lighting, and pneumatic sanding with two large capacity sandboxes on the boiler top.

Inaugural Train with the first 4-8-2 Locomotive at La Paz

The tender, which has a capacity of 6,000 gallons of water and 7¾ tons of oil fuel, is carried on two four-wheeled cast steel bogies, equipped with disc wheels and Timken roller - bearing axleboxes.

The locomotives were all shipped, dismantled and packed, to Antofagasta and were re-erected at the Mejillones Workshops of the Chilean Section of the railway.

INDIAN RAILWAYS

5ft.6in. Gauge   **1955**   **4-6-2 (WL)**

Cylinders	**(2) 19¼ in. Diam. X 28 in. Stroke**	Maximum Axleload		**16-9 tons**
Diameter Coupled Wheels	**5 ft. 7 in.**	Weight :		
		Engine in Working Order	**88-1**	"
Working Pressure	**210 lb.**	Tender " "	**62.59**	"
Tractive Effort at 85% Pressure	**27,640 lb.**	Total " "	**150-69**	"

The locomotive illustrated above, one of 10 constructed by The Vulcan Foundry in 1955, is a new prototype Pacific design with 16-9 tons axleload for medium passenger duties, built to the latest requirements of the Indian Railway Board, and designated as the WL Class. It bears no resemblance, however, to the WL locomotives delivered to the old North Western Railway in 1940.

Five of this new class have been sent for service to the Northern Railway of India and five to the Southern Railway. The boiler consists of a three-course barrel and round-topped firebox with combustion chamber. The inner shell is of all welded steel and has one thermic syphon and two arch tubes. A Joco regulator is fitted in the dome and the superheater has 30 elements.

Mountings include two Gresham & Craven No. 10 live steam injectors, three Ross Pop safety valves, two Everlasting blow-down cocks, and a drifting valve on the firebox back. The main frames are of 4¼ in. rolled steel bars and all axleboxes on both engine and tender are of roller-bearing type, five sets being of Timken manufacture and five of Skefko.

Spring compensation is provided between all the coupled and the hind truck axles.

The wheel centres of the engine bogie and truck are rolled steel discs and those of the tender are of pressed steel.

Cylinders are of cast steel with cast iron liners and each is made integral with half the smokebox saddle. On six engines all the crankpins are fitted with roller bearings, five by Timken and one by Skefko. The other four loco-motives have the Skefko type at the driving crankpin only. The valve motion is lubricated by soft grease throughout.

Other equipment includes a graduable steam brake valve, Stone's electric lighting, and Wakefield sight-feed lubricator.

The tender water tank is of rivetted construction and carries 4,500 gallons; the coal capacity is 12 tons.

EAST AFRICAN RAILWAYS

Metre Gauge   **1955**   **2-8-4 (Class)**

Cylinders	**(2) 17 in. Diam. X 26 in. Stroke**	Maximum Axleload	**11-35**	**tons**
Diameter Coupled Wheels	**4ft. 0 in**	Weight :		
		Engine in Working Order	**70-15**	"
Working Pressure	**200 lb**	Tender " "	**45.0**	"
Tractive Effort at 85% Pressure	**26,620 lb**	Total " "	**115.15**	"

In 1955 46 locomotives of new type were built by Vulcan for general service on all lines of the East African Railways and Harbours. Although the design is based on the original Nigerian River Class, the boiler and cylinders are somewhat smaller and these factors, together with a 2-8-4 wheel arrangement, permit an axleload of only 11-35 tons.

These engines are all oil-fired with two burners side by side at the front end of the firebox and are primarily for service in Kenya and Uganda. All of them are equipped with Westinghouse brakes, but five are provided with vacuum brake valves also so that they may be used in Tanganyika when required.

The boiler has a Belpaire firebox and all-welded steel inner shell and the 21 element superheater is equipped with a multi-valve regulator.

The 3¾ in. bar frames run the full length of the engine and are set in at both front and rear ends to allow for full swing over on the minimum curve of 330 ft. radius with | in. gauge widening.

Springing is compensated in two groups and all axles of both engine and tender have Timken roller-bearing axleboxes.

The leading truck has side control springs and the trailing truck is of the two-axle type with cast steel frame and rocker centering gear at each rear corner.

Each cast iron cylinder is made integral with half the smokebox saddle and bye-pass valves are located on the steamchests. Oil is fed to the valves and pistons by a Silvertown mechanical lubricator.

The main driving crankpins have Timken roller-bearings, but all the other crankpins revolve in gun-metal bushes, oil lubricated.

Skefko roller-bearings are fitted to the eccentric rods and the rest of the motion is lubricated by oil throughout.

General accessories include two Davies & Metcalfe No. 9 monitor injectors, two 3 in. Ross Pop safety valves, Klinger water gauges, Alfloc continuous blow-down valve, Everlasting blow-off cocks, M.C.A. couplers, Smiths-Stone speedometer, Lambert's sanding, and Stone's electric lighting.

The tender water and fuel tanks are of rivetted and welded construction and carry 4,130 gallons of water and 7¼ tons of oil fuel respectively.

These 46 locomotives are arranged for easy conversion from metre to 3 ft. 6 in. gauge if required, and all of them were shipped fully erected to the port of Mombasa.

List of Subscribers

M.M. Holmes Higgin, Barrow-in-Furness
Andrew Armstrong, Newton-le-Willows
Mrs Betty Taylor, Newton-le-Willows
Smiths of Wigan
Clive John Singleton, Newton-le-Willows
B. Robinson, Burtonwood, Warrington
Mr J McDonald , Newton-Le-Willows
Norman Arnold, Haydock, St Helens, Lancs
Mr. L.A. Harrison, Newton-le-Willows
Mrs B. Singleton, Newton-le-Willows
Mr. Stuart Pierce, Newton-le-Willows
Lane Head Newsagents, Lowton,
Mr. S. Smith, Newton-le-Willows
Mr P.A. Shawcross, Newton-le-Willows
Mr G. Moon, Winwick, Warrington
J.A. Sweetlove, Newton-le-Willows
Peter Simpson, Middleton, Manchester
Mr. R.F. Salmon, St Helens, Lancs
Colin Clough, Ashton-in-Makerfield, Lancs
St Helens Council, Housing Planning Dept.
Andrew Hughes, Newton-le-Willows
Mr J.K. Mahon, Newton-le-Willows
Wilfred Thompson, Newton-le-Willows
Mrs. D. Whamond, Newton-le-Willows
Newton News, Newton-le-Willows
Australian Railway Historical Society NSW

Norman Williams, Haydock, Lancs
Mr. R. Welding, Abergele, N. Wales
Mrs Beaney, Pennington, Leigh
Ian McDonald, Newton-le-Willows
Mr Jeff Houghton, Garswood, Wigan
Mrs Patricia Coulbourne, Warrington
Sean Kelly, Warrington, Cheshire
Roger Heath, Warrington, Cheshire
Mr Granger, Newton-le-Willows
Mr Lockyer, Newton-le-Willows
Mr Urmston, Newton-le-Willows
Mr Smith, Newton-le-Willows
Mrs Duffy, Newton-le-Willows
Mrs Whiteside, Newton-le-Willows
Mr Tarbrook, Newton-le-Willows
Mr Crinnigan, Newton-le-Willows
Mr Patton, Newton-le-Willows
Mrs Jolley, Newton-le-Willows
Jack Houghton, Newton-le-Willows
Andrew Marsh, Newton-le-Willows
Ian Templeton, Newton-le-Willows
Mr Corthwaite, Newton-le-Willows
Mr Ashcroft, Newton-le-Willows
Mr Irving, Newton-le-Willows
Edwards Newsagents, Newton-le-Willows